THE FIELD OF ROTATING MASSES

Previous books by the same author

The Evolution of Galaxies, Oliver & Boyd, 1967

The Physics of Stellar Interiors, Edinburgh University Press, 1974

Stellar Formation, Pergamon Press, 1978

The D-Force, published by the author, 1993

THE FIELD OF ROTATING MASSES

by

Vincent C. Reddish
O.B.E., D.Sc., Ph.D., B.Sc.(Hons), F.R.S.E.
Emeritus Professor of Astronomy, University of Edinburgh

MAKAR PUBLISHING
EDINBURGH

Published by
Makar Publishing
48/6 St. John's Road
Edinburgh, EH12 6PA
Scotland

The Field of Rotating Masses

ISBN 978-0-9551334-2-8

British Library Cataloguing in Publication data
A catalogue record for this book is available from the British Library

Design and pre-press production by
Makar Publishing Production

Printed and bound in the UK by Cromwell Press Group
Printed on paper from sustainable resources

Contents

List of Figures

Foreword

Dowsing, Divining and Fields Produced by Rotating Masses

Dowsing and Divining are different but interrelated subjects that have often been confused, and still are. In recent years, however, much more has become known about them as they have been studied by techniques well established in physics, particularly interferometry (Reddish, 1998, R. J. Dodd *et al.*, 2002).

An unexpected result of these studies is the discovery that all rotating masses – the sun, the planets and even masses as small as a bench grinder, generate a field the strength of which is proportional to the mass and to the angular speed of rotation. That is what this narrative is mostly about; it is written as a personal account of a research programme.

Abstract

The type of detectors used in this investigation were first demonstrated to me by a neighbour who used them to locate a blocked drain in my back yard. They are widely used by farmers, builders, archaeologists, dowsers and people working in the utility industries. See Figure 1.

I subsequently found that they always responded to linear structures above or below ground, and that parallel pairs of linear structures above ground produced patterns similar to those produced by two telescope radio astronomy interferometers and on a smaller scale by double slit optical interferometers (Fig. 2), indicating that the structures and detectors are responding to a transverse wave radiation field.

The patterns produced by them varied with time of year. Compact interferometers introduced by C. M. Humphries made it possible to measure the pattern indoors or out throughout the year, and in both hemispheres (Fig. 11).

If the interferometer is shielded from the sun by aluminium foil or crossed sheets of stretched polyethylene film, the pattern disappears. If a rotating mass such as a bench grinder is placed between the shield and the interferometer, the pattern reappears.

Crossed sheets of stretched polyethylene film do not block the field of a rotating mass if they are part of it; aluminium foil does. Consequently the former do not block the earth's field but the latter does. In a laboratory the foil is covered by crossed stretched polyethylene films to prevent internal reflections.

In a laboratory fully shielded from the solar and earth fields, two rotating masses are required to reproduce the interferometer pattern. If the angle between the axes of rotation is changed progressively from 0° to 90°, the spacing of the pattern changes between 2 m and 6 m. If a carton of water is placed between the rotating masses, the change in the spacing happens suddenly when the angle between the axes goes through 45° (Figs. 9 and 10).

It is concluded that the dowsing phenomenon results from a field produced by the rotation of the sun interacting with a field from the earth, that the annual change in the interferometer fringe pattern spacing from 2 m to 6 m is due to the change in the relative inclinations of the axes of rotation of the sun and the earth as the earth orbits the sun, and the suddenness of the change is due to the water in the oceans.

Introduction to the Physics of Dowsing

Dowsing as a means of locating underground pipes and cables is widely used by people in the building, farming and utility industries; dowsing rods were first demonstrated to me by a neighbour who used them to locate a blocked drain in my back yard.

The discovery that parallel pairs of horizontal linear structures above ground produce patterns of dowsing response in the form of parallel equally spaced lines typical of interferometry (Reddish, 1993, 1998) made it possible to investigate dowsing using a technique well established in experimental physics.

Divining is a more specialised technique which most ordinary dowsers like me cannot do. A simple experiment that illustrates a difference between them and can be carried out by ordinary dowsers is described below.

Lay a hosepipe on the ground, and walk across it carrying dowsing rods. The rods will detect the linear structure (dowsing works equally well with structures under, on, or above ground). Now connect the hosepipe to a water supply, turn on the water supply, and walk across the pipe again; the rods will rotate as before. Lift up the end of the hose so that the water will not drain out and turn off the supply so that the hosepipe is full of still water. Walk across it and the rods will rotate. Now (and this is the crucial part of the experiment) stand still on the pipe holding the dowsing rods as usual and ask someone to turn on the water supply; the rods will rotate as the water flows.

Another similar experiment is of interest for different reasons. Lay the hosepipe in a circle. The dowsing rods will rotate not only when the dowser is stood still on the pipe and the water supply is turned on, but also if the dowser stands still in the exact centre of the circle, but nowhere else. This is of course similar to the effect that would be produced if the pipe was replaced by a cable carrying electricity and the magnetic field was measured but, as noted below, it has been established beyond doubt that the dowsing field is not electromagnetic.

Dowsers can detect any linear structures such as pipes, drains, cables, the edges of old roads, buried foundations of old buildings, underground waterways whether or not there is water in them, and so on. Diviners, it appears, are a special minority who are particularly sensitive to the flow of water and can detect it while walking.

Dowsing Interferometry strongly suggests that dowsing utilises a transverse wave radiation field (Reddish 1993, 1998). Since the horizontal linear structures of the interferometer can be of copper, steel, or pvc, the field is clearly not electromagnetic. This was confirmed by carrying out the interferometry in an electromagnetically shielded laboratory courtesy of BAE at Edinburgh (Reddish, 1998).

Early in the interferometry it was also found that the pattern varies with time, and it will be shown in Chapter 3(iii) that water has an important effect on the interferometer pattern.

The development by C. M. Humphries of compact interferometers that can be used indoors or out made it possible to measure the interference pattern daily for long periods of time in both hemispheres, showing that the variations with time are very systematic and similar in both hemispheres, but inverted with respect to each other (Dodd *et al.*, 2002). Figure 2 in that reference – the data are reproduced in Figure 11 – provides evidence of the high level of repeatability that can be obtained with this system of measurement. This alone is sufficient to establish the reality and usefulness of dowsing, both as a tool and as a means of research. The rods and interferometers were of similar materials and size in both hemispheres, and the results were communicated a month in arrears so that they were completely independent of each other.

At an early stage in the dowsing experiments it was found that aluminium behaved differently from other materials being used such as copper, steel, wood and pvc (Reddish, 1993, 1998). Also, when dowsing an overhead cable the field appeared to be radiated perpendicularly from the ground surface (Reddish, 1993, Fig. 4, reproduced below). It occurred to me that aluminium

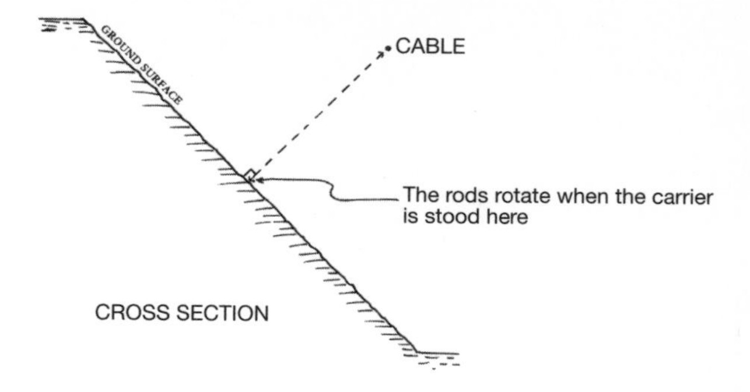

foil on the soles of the feet might prevent the dowsing field from entering the body and thus prevent the dowsing rods from rotating. This proved to be the case. Soon after, other dowsers reported to me similar experiments, one going so far as to cover himself completely with aluminium foil. All found that dowsing was prevented. Another reported to me that tin plate had the same effect, which I confirmed.

The possibility thus arose that aluminium foil or tin plate could be used to shield a compact interferometer from any fields coming from the sun and the earth and thus prevent it from forming the fringe pattern, and this proved to be correct. It was then a simple matter to show that aluminium foil reflected the field by using it to reflect the field from the sun to the interferometer behind the screen and re-establish the interferometer pattern (it had been found early in the dowsing experiments that wood, hardboard and cardboard are transparent to the dowsing field so it is always easy to shield from light).

The interferometer pattern had already been interpreted as evidence that the field is a transverse wave radiation field. Consequently it should be polarised by reflection and eliminated by cross polarisation, and this was confirmed.

Fields Produced by Rotating Masses

As noted above, the dowsing field appears to be a transverse wave radiation field and the field is not electromagnetic. The question then arose, what is the nature and origin of the field? The further interferometry carried out simultaneously in Scotland and in New Zealand (Fig. 11), showed that the dowsing field is world wide, suggesting the possibility that the field is created in or by the earth, and consequently similarly by the other planets and perhaps by the sun as well.

The possibility that the angular momentum of rotating masses creates a field had long been a matter of speculation but most theoretical investigations had predicted that any such field would be weak and none had ever been found, although what form such a field would take and how it could be detected were questions that appear not to have been addressed.

If the worldwide nature of the dowsing field correctly implies that it is created by the rotation of the earth (and consequently by the other planets as well as by the sun), the implication is that dowsing rods provide a detector for the field produced by rotating masses and the dowsing interferometry shows that the field is a transverse wave radiation field, answering the questions raised in the previous paragraph. It has also been shown that the field is not electromagnetic.

Experiments using a rotating mass – a bench grinder purchased from a do-it-yourself store – showed immediately that it did indeed produce a field to which dowsing rods responded and which is reflected by aluminium foil, as is the dowsing field.

However, to be sure that the dowsing field is created by rotating masses, and is not some other kind of field coming from the sun and from the earth to which dowsing rods also respond, it was necessary to experiment with fields produced by rotating masses in a laboratory shielded from the fields of the sun and the earth, in particular to see if rotating masses radiate a field that produces a similar interference pattern. The problem with using aluminium foil as a shield was that since it reflects the field produced by a rotating mass the laboratory would be filled with internal reflections.

About this time an article by two Russian authors, Nacholov and Parkhamov, appeared on the Internet reporting that stretched polyethylene film (commonly used as 'clingfilm' in Britain for wrapping food) polarises torsion radiation, a comprehensive term used by them and their colleagues that supposedly includes fields produced by rotating masses. This seemed to me then to be a remarkable discovery, and still does. I was sufficiently suspicious to want to confirm it and that was easily done by polarising the field by reflection with aluminium and cross-polarising by transmission through stretched polyethylene film, which eliminated the field (having first established that the film transmitted the unpolarised field).

In the course of creating a shielded laboratory, described in detail in Chapter 2, further discoveries were made relating to the polarisation by stretched polyethylene film, a least two of them being of wider interest.

Firstly, each batch of film was tested as above to ensure that it polarised; not all did.

Secondly, it was found that although the crossed polarising films effectively blocked the field produced by a rotating mass when they were placed between the rotating mass and the dowser, they did not block the field if they were wrapped round the mass and rotated with it.

So although they block the solar field they are not expected to block the earth's field.

We cannot be sure that any field we detect coming from the earth has been produced by the earth; because we, the laboratory and our instruments are all part of the rotating mass, and it is not evident that we could detect a field produced by a rotating mass of which we are part. It could, perhaps, be the field from the sun retransmitted, scattered or reflected by the earth.

Fields produced by rotating masses have recently become even more controversial as a result of articles published by the Russian Academy of Science under the all embracing title of torsion fields; the experiments described here using rotating masses are as different from theirs as classical physics is from quantum physics and the Russian arguments are not relevant to them.

Anyone who wishes to repeat or extend the experiments described in this book but has not yet learned to dowse, would be well advised to learn on farms or building sites where dowsing is used for practical purposes by people who would not waste time using things that don't work.

CHAPTER 1

A Brief History of Dowsing Interferometry

The discovery that vertically disposed pairs of horizontal linear structures produce patterns of parallel lines of dowsing response (Reddish, 1993) provided an explanation of patterns that had been rediscovered many times by dowsers, and had even led to speculation that they might be interference patterns; but no-one had pursued the matter.

A few years involved in radio astronomy interferometry in the Nuffield Radio Astronomy Laboratory at Jodrell Bank had given me an understanding of how much we might learn about the dowsing phenomenon by the application of a tool so well established in experimental physics, with the advantage that the means to do so in this case were cheap and easy to develop.

The technique of dowsing had been demonstrated to me by someone with considerable experience of its use in an area of the Central Highlands of Scotland where it is widely used on farms, building sites, and in the electricity and water industries. The material necessary for making a pair of dowsing rods – galvanised fencing wire – is readily available there.

Hand held rods of various materials, usually wood or metal, have been used successfully for centuries to locate underground structures of many kinds (Georgius Agricola, *De Re Metallica*, 1556). An illustration of how to make and hold the L-shaped rods typically used today in pairs, one in each hand, on farms, building sites and utilities, is given below in Figure 1. They have been used in all the experiments by Reddish, and by Dodd, Harris, Humphries and Reddish described in this publication, and by colleagues who have joined with them to form what has become known as the Dowsing Physics Group.

How the rods are held is particularly important, because different holds have been found to detect different patterns of interference fringes; the hold shown in Fig.1 is the one used for all the measurements shown in this publication.

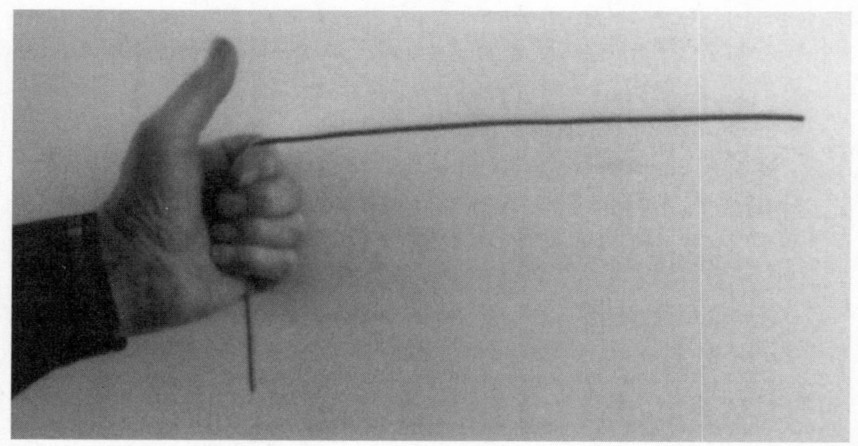

Figure 1 The standard L-shaped dowsing rod made of galvanised fencing wire – usually 2 mm or 3 mm in diameter. The way it is held with the thumb up is of importance and is standard practice within the Dowsing Physics Group; if the rod is held with the thumb round, a different set of interference fringes is detected.

The first interferometer was constructed in pastureland by Loch Rannoch in the Scottish Central Highlands and is illustrated in Figure 2. The measured patterns it produced provided the first evidence that dowsing utilises a transverse wave radiation field and that the spacing of the pattern changes with time. This large interferometer was subsequently replaced by a compact and more convenient design developed by C. M. Humphries (Fig. 3), which made possible the subsequent worldwide study of the interference patterns and then the laboratory studies of the patterns produced by the field of rotating masses.

The results of the worldwide study of the interference patterns is shown in Figure 11. The laboratory studies of the field produced by rotating masses is the subject of the following chapters.

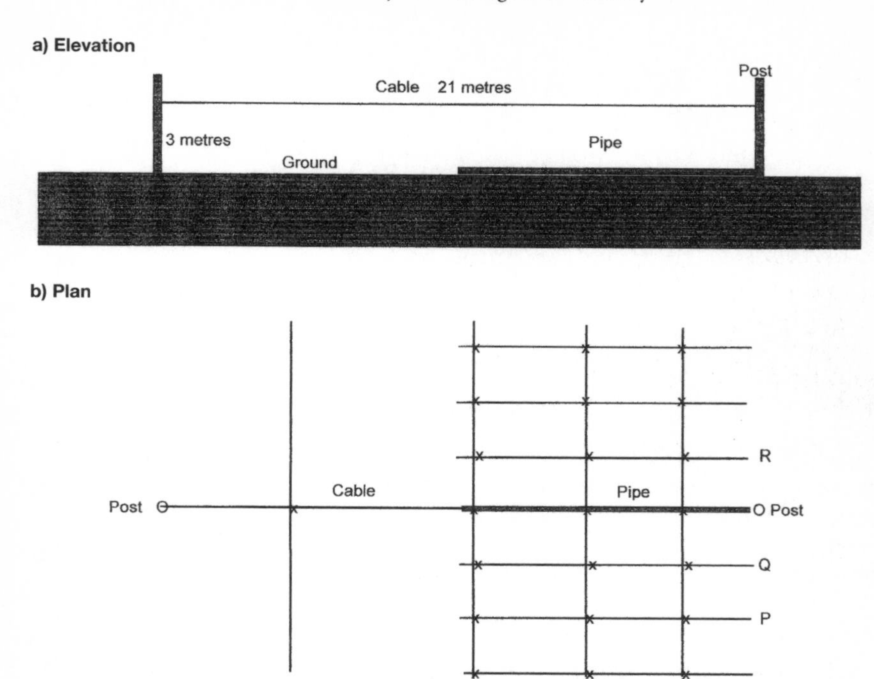

Figure 2 The first dowsing interferometer. When the dowsing rods were carried under the cable along track A they rotated only below the cable, but when they were carried along tracks B, C, and D between the cable and the pipe, they rotated at regular intervals x, forming the pattern of lines P, Q, R, etc. The presence of the pattern is evidence that the linear structures – pipe and cable – interact with a transverse wave radiation field to create standing waves.

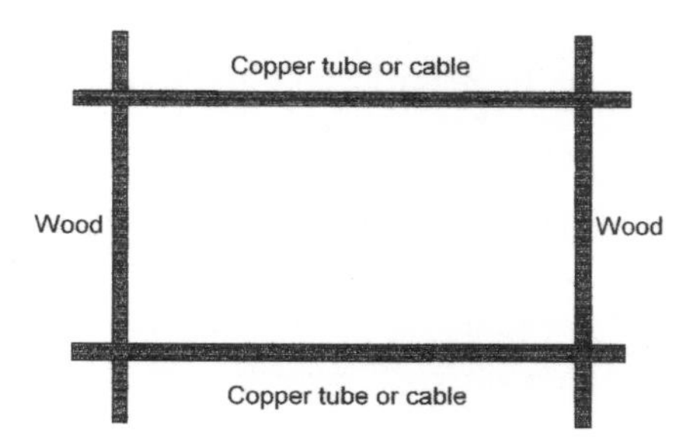

Figure 3 The compact interferometer first introduced by C. M. Humphries. The length and separation of the copper tubes or cables should be not less than 60 cm.

CHAPTER 2

The Laboratory

(i) Construction of a Shielded Laboratory, stage one

The framework of the laboratory was of timber and it was constructed in a brick built garage. Timber and brick had already been found to be transparent to the dowsing field.

The laboratory was not shielded completely in one operation, but it was done in two stages.

In the first stage the laboratory was lined with crossed stretched polyethylene films, already tested for polarising effectiveness as described above, placed between sheets of hardboard in order to protect them from physical damage, and to test their effectiveness in shielding the laboratory from external fields. All six internal surfaces of the laboratory, four walls including the door, floor and ceiling, were lined. An electrical power cable was led in through a small hole to provide power for lighting and for the rotating masses.

The laboratory was fitted with the following equipment to carry out the experiments.

1. A compact interferometer made of two parallel horizontal copper tubes of diameter 15 mm in a vertical plane attached to the east wall by pvc clips screwed to the wall with steel screws. The tubes had the following dimensions:

length	60 cm (half the width of the lab.);
height of lower tube from floor	5 cm;
height of upper tube from floor	65 cm.

2. Two pairs of rotating masses, workshop bench grinders, each with properties as follows:

Twin grinding wheels on a common axis

wheel diameter	150 mm;
thickness	20 mm;
mass	800 g;
separation	227 mm;
rotation speed	2900 rpm.

Henceforth, each of the above will be referred to simply as the generator.

3. A pair of 45° mirrors made of aluminium foil on hardboard designed to reflect the field from the generators and the interferometer, along the laboratory and back, to give a longer path length for measuring the interferometer fringe patterns.

All of these features are shown in plan on Figures 4A and 4B.

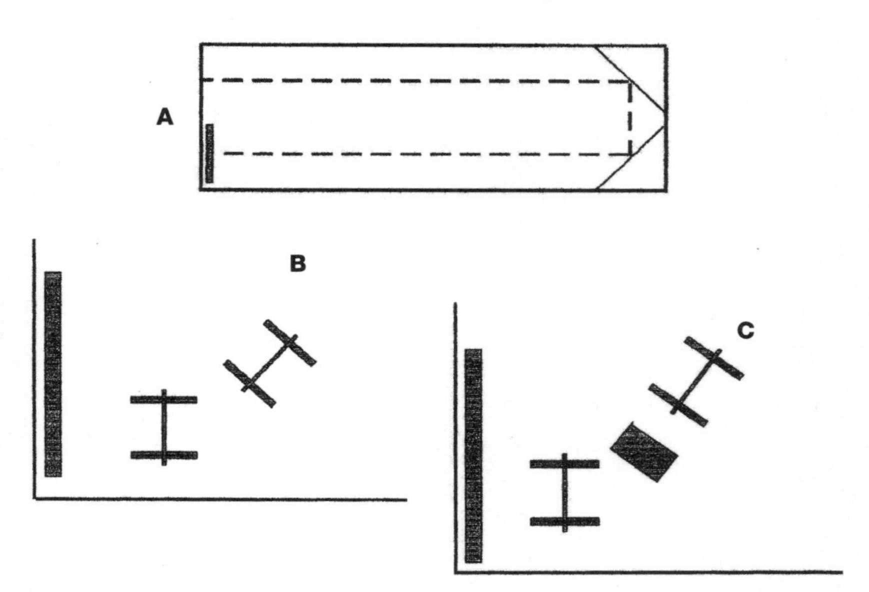

Figure 4 A) Plan of the shielded laboratory with a compact interferometer in a vertical plane at one end and two 45° aluminium mirrors to give a track length of 7 m. **B)** Plan view of the comer of the shielded laboratory with a compact interferometer in a vertical plane and two generators, one rotated about a vertical axis. **C)** As in **B** but with the addition of a 5 litre water container.

(ii) The Fields produced by Rotating Masses, outside and inside the stage one laboratory

The very considerable experience I and my colleagues have in the use of dowsing detector rods made it sensible to use them in these experiments; as noted in the introduction we have good reason to be confident of measurements made with them and they give immediate results. Furthermore, it is obviously necessary to use them if we are to establish that the dowsing field and the field produced by rotating masses are identical, as suggested in the Introduction.

It had already been found that the generator produces a field to which dowsing rods respond and which is reflected by aluminium foil (tests were made also to ensure that it did not produce any detectable electric or magnetic fields).

The way to make and use dowsing rods was described and illustrated in Chapter 1.

When the generator is placed outside the laboratory and switched on, dowsing rods rotate when they are carried across the line of the axis or the lines of the planes of the discs (Fig. 5). When the generator is switched off, the dowsing rods response disappears, not instantly but persisting for a few minutes after the generator rotation has ceased. Dowsing interference patterns similarly decay slowly when the interferometer is removed (Reddish, 1993).

If crossed polarisers are placed across the line between the generator and the experimenter with the detector rods, that field is not detected.

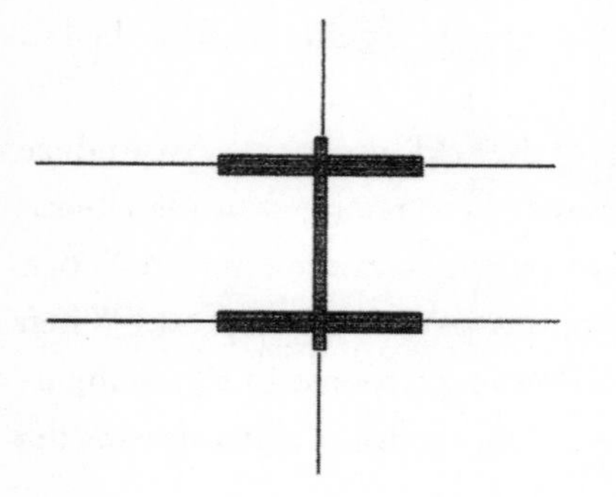

Figure 5 Plan view of a generator (a twin wheel bench grinder) irradiated by the fields of the sun and the earth. Dowsing detector rods rotate when they are carried across the line of the axis or the planes of the discs, mapping lines as shown which extend indefinitely.

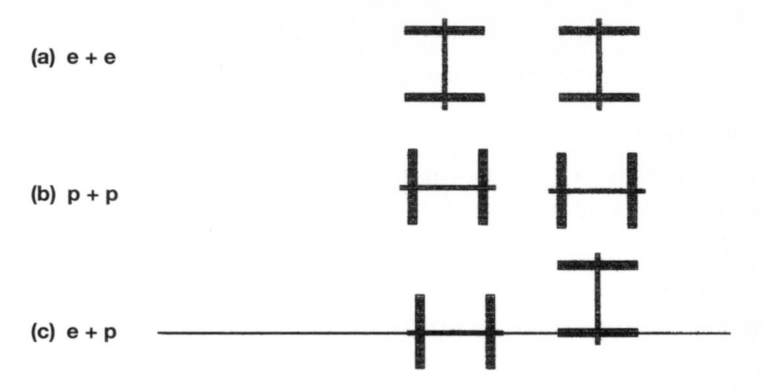

Figure 6 Pairs of generators in the shielded laboratory. The only dowsing response is across the line shown in **(c)** e + p.

If crossed polarisers are placed between the generator and the sun, none of the fields is detected. Note that this is true at any time of the day or night, confirming that the field from the sun passes through the earth (for obvious reasons experiments at night, inside or out, were always carried out with artificial light).

This suggests that perhaps two sources of the field, one irradiating the other such as the sun irradiating the earth, or the sun irradiating a generator, are required to produce a dowsing response.

To establish uniformity in terminology between the laboratory experiments and planetary systems, the axis of rotation of a spinning mass (such as the generator) will be referred to as the pole, and the bisecting plane perpendicular to the axis, as the equator; corresponding fields are described as p-fields and e-fields.

To test the possibility that two sources of the field are necessary to produce a detector response two identical generators were arranged in the laboratory – successively in each of the three orientations shown in Figure 6. When only one of the pair was switched on there was no dowsing response. When both were switched on there was still no dowsing response in the configurations e + e (a) and p + p (b) but there was a strong response when crossing the

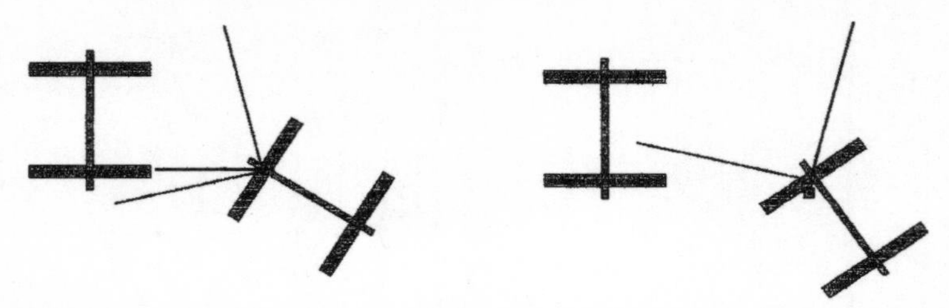

Figure 7 Compare to Figure 6. When either generator is rotated in a horizontal plane by less than ±45° the dowsing response still occurs across a line joining the pole of one to the disc of the other; but when it is rotated by more than ±45° the dowsing response disappears.

line e + p shown in (c). The same results were obtained when the directions of spin of either or both were reversed. By rotating the spin axis of either generator in a horizontal plane in the last of the three configurations, the angle over which the dowsing response occurs can be measured; it is found to be ±45° arc in each case (Fig. 7). Note that within the ±45° arc the detector response occurs only when crossing the line joining the pole of one generator to the disc of the other.

Early in the development of dowsing interferometers it was found that aluminium behaved differently to copper and many other materials used in their construction (Reddish, 1993, and see pp. 2, 3). Further experiments by the author showed that tin, silver and gold behaved like aluminium, and added more materials to the copper-like group (Reddish, 1998, Table 3 and Section 4.2). C. M. Humphries (Pers. Comm., 1999) discovered the reason for these different behaviours by showing that aluminium reflects the interferometer pattern whereas copper transmits it. Consequently, it is of interest to know if these materials behave in this way with respect to the fields produced by rotating masses.

An effect similar to Figure 6c can be obtained by using one generator and three aluminium mirrors, as shown in Figure 8. Each mirror is a sheet of hardboard covered with a single sheet of aluminium foil.

There is a dowsing response when the generator is switched on and the detector rods are carried across any part of the line connecting the pole to the equator of the generator via the mirrors.

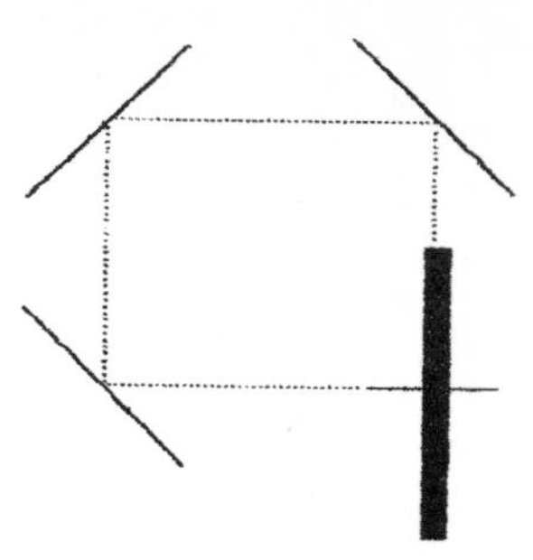

Figure 8 A single generator using three 45° aluminium mirrors to bring the p and e fields into coincidence. Dowsing detector rods rotate when they are carried across any position on the dotted line shown.

This provides an arrangement suitable for testing the reflectivity and transmission of materials to radiation produced by rotating masses. To test for transmission a sheet of the material is placed across the line at any point; if the material is opaque to the field the dowsing response is annulled everywhere along the line; if it transmits, the dowsing response is unaltered. To test for reflection one of the mirrors is replaced by a sheet of the material; if it reflects, the dowsing response remains; if it transmits, the dowsing response is annulled.

In this way, it was found that copper, pvc, wood and steel transmit the field, whereas aluminium, tin and silver reflect it. The results are the same as those obtained for the dowsing field outside the laboratory.

The arrangement is also useful for other experiments; for example, finding the effect of changing the mass, or composition, or speed of rotation of the mass, in the generator.

Given the nature of the detector, any change in the strength of the field could only be an estimate. When the generator was switch off the field decreased in strength as the generator slowed down, apparently proportional to the speed of rotation. If the mass was increased or decreased the strength of the field again appeared to change in proportion. The most difficult experiments were those measuring the effect of changing the material because of the need to keep the mass constant; the limitations of the detector – being unable to give a quantitative measurement of the strength of the field greatly limited the range of materials that could be used. Within that limited range, change of material with mass and speed of rotation unchanged did not appear to change the strength of the field.

Outside the laboratory a single pipe or cable, overhead or below ground, gives a dowsing response when walking across the line of it. Inside the stage one shielded laboratory it is convenient to use an overhead copper pipe; this is placed just above head level across the laboratory and gives no dowsing response when walking underneath across the line of it. When the pipe and the floor beneath it are irradiated by a single generator the pipe gives a good dowsing response. However, when a crossed polarising screen is placed so that the generator irradiates the pipe but not the floor beneath it, there is no dowsing response.

(iii) Interferometry inside the stage one laboratory, including the effects of the earth's field as well as the solar field

Outside the laboratory, the interferometer produces fringes with a spacing depending on time of year as shown on Figure 11. Inside the laboratory the interferometer does not produce fringes until it is irradiated by a generator, and with its spin axis either parallel or perpendicular to the vertical plane of the interferometer it always produces a fringe pattern of the same spacing as that produced outside which is dependent on the time of year. As previously noted in Section (ii), two sources of radiation appear to be necessary to create a dowsing response, but in these first experiments carried out in the stage one shielded laboratory using an interferometer, irradiation by only one generator was needed to create a fringe pattern. The time dependent similarity between the inside and outside implies that some effect, perhaps some other field, determines the fringe spacing and that it is not blocked by the crossed polarising filters The author is confident that the field due to the rotation of the sun is blocked by the crossed polarising filters – many experiments have confirmed this conclusion – but the experiments in Section (ii) suggest that perhaps the fields radiated by the earth are not similarly blocked.

There is an important difference between using a crossed polariser filter to block the field from the sun and using it to block the fields from the earth; the filter is attached to the earth and is rotating with it.

To find out if this makes a difference, two generators in the arrangement of Figure 6c were used in the laboratory. First, the steel protecting cowl covering the rotating disc at the bottom right of the Figure was wrapped with crossed stretched polyethylene film polariser material; the generators were switched on but the dowsing response along the line shown was annulled. This wrapping was then removed and put on the disc so that it would rotate with it; the generators were switched on and the dowsing response appeared as usual. This confirms that if crossed film polarisers are rotating with a mass producing a field they do not block it; therefore they should not be expected to block the earth's fields as they do that of the sun.

The experiment was repeated using aluminium foil instead of crossed films. It made no difference whether the foil was wrapped round the protecting steel cowl or round the rotating disc; in either case the dowsing response did not appear when the generators were switched on. It is concluded that aluminium foil blocks all fields produced by rotating masses, those of the earth as well as those of the sun.

(iv) The fully shielded laboratory

Following these experiments, shielding by aluminium foil to block the earth fields was added to the laboratory to produce the fully shielded laboratory.

In the first instance this was only put on the floor and up the walls to a level equal to the height of the top of the interferometer, which was above the top of the generators. To avoid internal reflection of fields produced by the generators, the aluminium foil was covered by crossed stretched polyethylene film. No fields from the earth could then irradiate the generators or the interferometer. This made it possible to test the supposition that the change in the fringe spacing from 6 m to 2 m is due to interaction of a field from the earth with the interferometer as well as the field from the generator.

The experiment using the compact interferometer irradiated by a ***single*** generator described in the first paragraph of Section (iii) above was repeated and it no longer produced an interferometer pattern, confirming that the above supposition was correct, and also that the last paragraph in Section (iii) was correct.

CHAPTER 3

Experiments in the Laboratory

Interferometry inside the fully shielded laboratory, includes:

(i) a fixed interferometer and a pair of generators;

(ii) changing the angle between the axes of spin of pairs of rotating masses; and

(iii) introducing water between them, to mimic more closely the relationship between the sun and the earth;

(iv) errors.

(i) A fixed interferometer and a pair of generators

The compact interferometer fixed in a vertical plane was irradiated by two generators with their spin axes horizontal and parallel to each other and to the plane of the interferometer. When either one of the generators is switched on no interference fringes are produced, but when both are switched on a fringe is detected close to 6 m.

(ii) Changing the angle between the axes of spin of pairs of rotating masses

The spin axis of one of the generators was then rotated in a horizontal plane about a vertical axis (Fig. 4b), and the fringe spacing decreased to 2 m (with fringes at 2 m, 4 m and 6 m) when the angle between the spin axes was 45° (Fig. 9a). The fringe spacing increased with further rotation, reaching 6m again at 90°.

If, with the spin axes kept parallel or orthogonal to each other, the pair of generators is rotated about a vertical axis in increments from 0° to 90° (i.e. rotated relative to the plane of the interferometer) the fringe spacing remains at 6 m. If the spin axes are kept at 45° to each other and the pair is rotated similarly, the fringe spacing remains at 2 m.

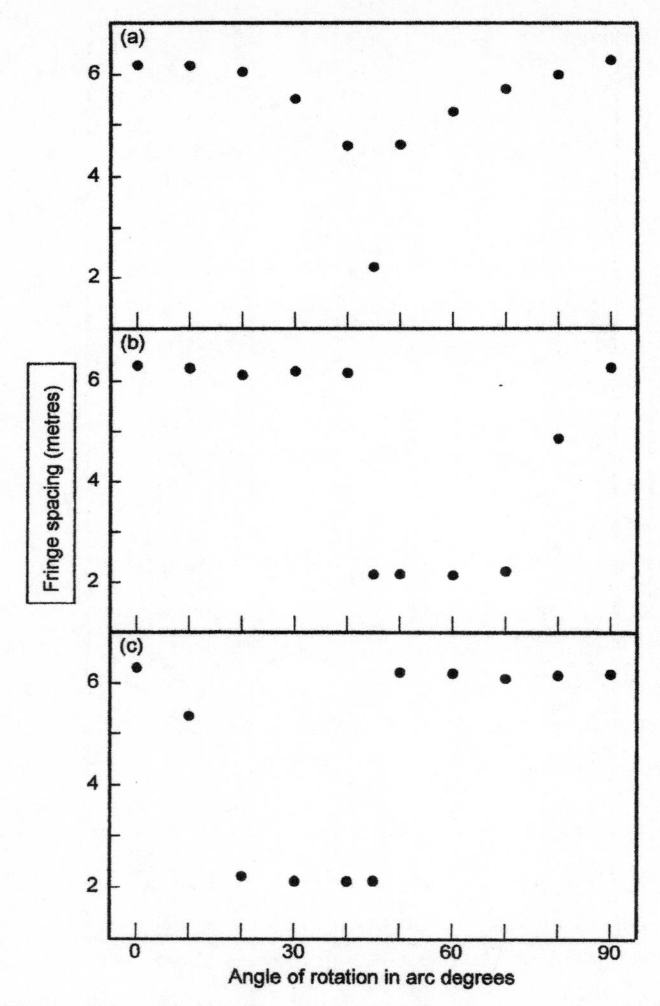

Figure 9 **(a)** A compact interferometer fixed in a vertical plane in the fully shielded laboratory, irradiated by two generators with their spin axes horizontal and parallel to the plane of the interferometer. The spin of axis one is then rotated about a vertical axis; see Figure 4b, 2000 November 4, when the fringe spacing on Figure 11 is 6m. **(b)** As in Figure 9a but with a 5 litre container of water placed close to the end of the spin axis of the generator being rotated; see Figure 4c. The direction of rotation is anticlockwise from 0° to 90°; 2000 November 4. **(c)** As in Figure 9b but rotated in the reverse direction from 90° to 0°; 2000 November 2.

Compare (b) and (c) with Figure 11.

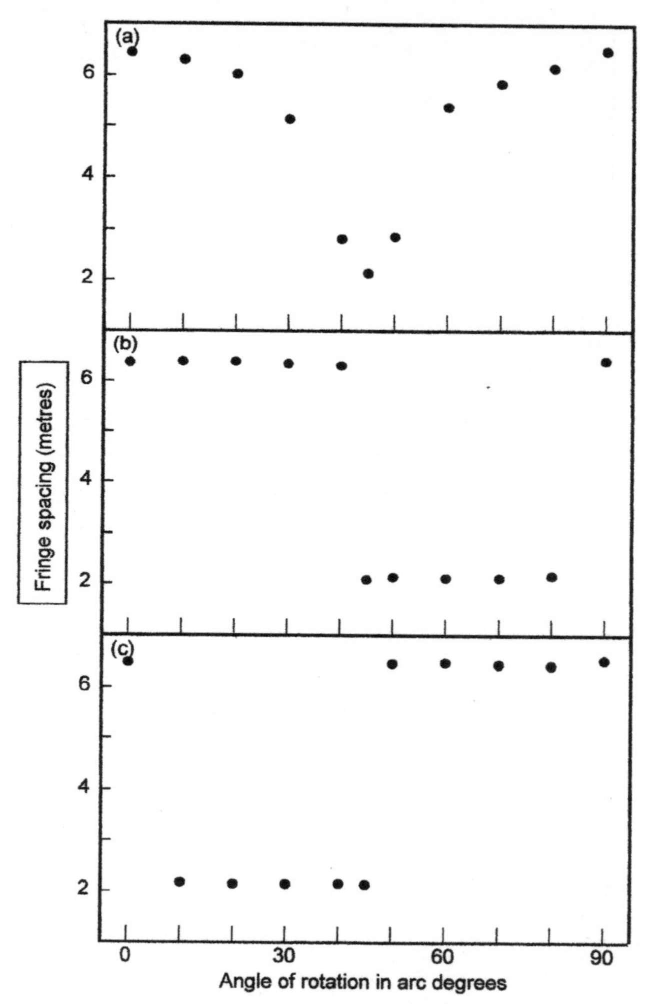

Figure 10 (a) As in Figure 9a but measured on 29 November 2000 after the fringe spacing outside (see Figure 11) had changed from 6 m to 2 m. The change outside has not affected the measurements in the fully shielded laboratory. **(b)** As in Figure 9b with the water container in place, but measured after the November event when the fringe spacing measured outside the fully shielded laboratory has reduced from 6 m to 2 m. **(c)** Measured in the reverse direction and with the water container in place as in Figure 9c, but after the November event when the fringe spacing measured outside the laboratory has reduced from 6 m to 2 m.

Compare (b) and (c) with Figure 11.

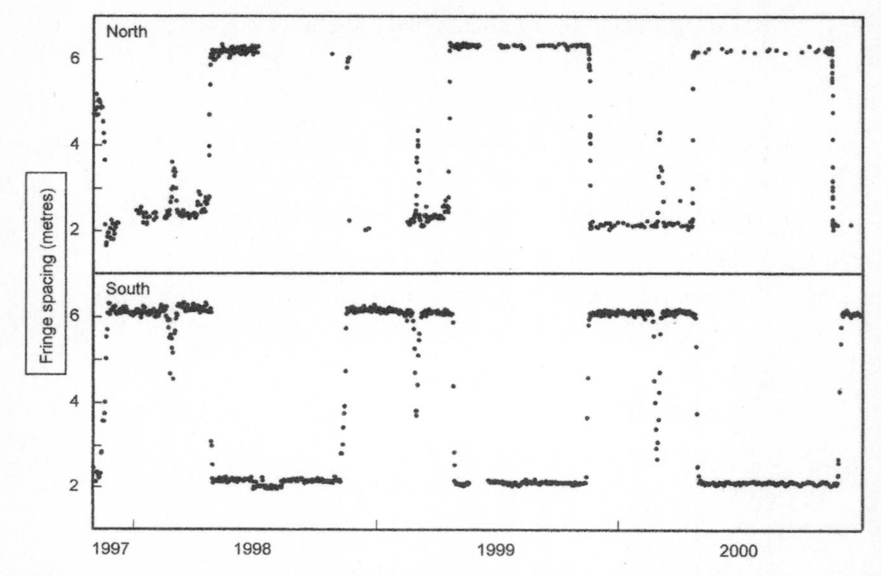

Figure 11 Dowsing interferometer fringe spacings measured in the northern and southern hemispheres (Scotland and New Zealand; Dodd *et al.*, 2002). The pattern is inverted in one hemisphere with respect to the other. It is notably stable inbetween the sudden changes in April and in November except for the isolated event in March. In Figures 9 and 10, all the measurements were made in Scotland, in some cases at times when the fringe spacing in the north on this figure is 2 m, in others when it is 6 m, as noted in the captions.

These results again indicate that the annual change in the interferometer fringe spacing between 2 m and 6 m outside the laboratory is due to the change in the angle between the fields of the sun and the earth by 47° from winter to summer. However, the annual changes happen suddenly (Fig. 11), whereas all these experiments with interferometers, inside and out, have produced fringe spacings that change gradually with the angle between the generators.

The relatively sudden changes on Figure 11 beg the question as to whether some other factor is involved. The atmosphere is too unstable to give a pattern so smoothly repetitive; the molten core of the earth seems a less likely candidate than the oceans and is certainly much harder to simulate in laboratory experiments. The decision to try water first is an obvious one.

(iii) A fixed interferometer, two generators and water

The experiments are the same as those above, but with the addition of a 5 litre container of water placed at the end of the spin axis of the generator being rotated (Fig. 4c). The dependence of the interferometer fringe spacing on angle of rotation of the axis is shown in Figure 9b. It gives the surprising result that it remains constant at 6 m from 0° to 40° and then decreases suddenly to 2 m at 45°, remaining at that value through 70° then rising to 6 m at 90°.

When the measurement is made in the reverse direction from 90° to 0°, the pattern is mirror imaged (Fig. 9c).

These experiments reproduce the features of the dowsing field interferometer patterns for the northern and southern latitudes shown in Figure 11.

It was pointed out in Chapter 2(iii) that in the stage one shielded laboratory, prior to introducing aluminium to shield from the earth's field, the fringe spacing measured inside changed when the outside pattern changed, in April from 2m to 6m and in late November from 6 m to 2 m. The measurements in Figure 9 were made when the fringe spacing outside was 6m and it was therefore of interest to repeat the measurements after the November event, when the fringe spacing outside had decreased to 2 m. This was done and the results, given in Figure 10, are essentially the same as those in Figure 9 and confirm that with the aluminium shielding the laboratory is shielded from both the solar and earth fields.

Because of the need to carry out these experiments during the annual events when the dowsing interferometer pattern spacing changes, both with and without the aluminium shielding as well as with the crossed stretched polyethylene film, and to have the time to make the necessary changes to the laboratory, these experiments took about three years to complete.

Referring back to Figure 6, it was found that, if the 5 litre container of water was introduced into the assemblies 6a or 6b, dowsing responses were obtained. It appears that when water is irradiated by a p-field or an e-field, it emits both a p-field and an e-field; measurements made on all sides of the water container show that it emits both fields in all directions and they are not polarised.

Several other liquids have been similarly tested but none of them have shown this effect.

(iv) **Errors**

The results given in the Figures are affected by three types of experimental error – random errors of measurement, distortion, and the pattern retention effect

Random errors of measurement determined by repetition are generally about ±0.02 m and are a measure of the accuracy with which the detector system locates the position of an individual interference fringe.

Irregularities in the ground surface or the presence of isolated masses have been shown to distort the interference pattern considerably (Reddish, 1998, Fig. 3). The effect of the built environment on such patterns can be expected to be at least as severe but more complex and are probably responsible for the asymmetries that occurred in interference patterns obtained in the stage one shielded laboratory. Support for this conclusion is provided by the absence of such asymmetries in Figures 9 and 10, showing measurements carried out in the fully shielded laboratory, and thus confirming that the interior of that laboratory was isolated from external fields.

The pattern decay effect in dowsing interferometry (Reddish 1993, 1998) is particularly troublesome when changes are made to an interferometer – such as rotating it – causing distortions in the fringe pattern when the change is small and instabilities when the change is large. The time scales involved range from minutes to hours and for any particular experimental arrangement and environment can only be found by repetitive experiments. This has been done for all the experiments described in this paper so that the effect is reduced to a level comparable to or less than the random errors of measurement.

CHAPTER 4

Discussion

It is not possible, of course, to model exactly the sun-earth system in the laboratory. What has been attempted in this investigation is to examine some of the factors that appear to be relevant to understanding the pattern of dowsing measurements in Figure 11.

It was pointed out in Chapter 2(iii) that replacing the solar field with one produced by a generator had the surprising result that it did not affect the interferometer pattern. This conclusion was reinforced by shielding the interferometer from the earth's field as well as from the solar field by using aluminium foil, and introducing a second generator, again producing no change to the fringe spacing. The interferometer patterns have been shown to depend on the geometry and materials of the interferometer (Reddish, 1993) but, for the types of interferometer used in this investigation at least, the fringe spacing is independent of the mass, size, composition or angular speed of the rotating bodies – earth, sun or generator – producing the fields. Two interacting fields, natural or artificial, are required to produce a dowsing response.

In Chapter 3 it was shown that if both the earth's and the sun's fields are replaced by generators with the laboratory completely shielded from natural sources of radiation, the interferometer pattern does not depend on time of year but the fringe spacing remains in the range 2 m to 6 m. Subsidiary experiments have confirmed that these fringe spacings are not affected by changes in the mass, size, composition or angular speeds of the rotating discs. The fringe spacings are, however, dependent on the angle between the spin axes of the rotating discs, and this dependence is altered if water is introduced into the system.

Comparison of Figures 9b, 9c, 10b and 10c with Figure 11 indicates that the sudden change in the fringe spacings in April and in November, and the mirror imaging of the northern and southern patterns, result from the interaction of the rotation fields of the sun and the earth, the change in the angle between the spin axes of the sun and the earth during the year as the earth orbits the sun, and the effect of the earth's oceans and inland waters.

The sudden changes in fringe spacing between 2 m and 6 m on Figures 9 and 10 occur at 45°, when the boundaries between the e- and p-fields of one generator are respectively perpendicular and parallel to the axis of the other generator (see Fig. 7). Perhaps some such boundary between the earth fields interacts with the solar field in a similar manner.

The isolated event at the beginning of March (Fig. 11), also mirror imaged in the northern and southern hemispheres, remains a mystery. Since it recurs at the same position of the earth in its orbit about the sun each year it seems likely that it results from the earth crossing a line of interaction between the sun and some other source of radiation outside the solar system (see Fig. 7).

As noted above, the radiation from the sun passes through the earth. Nevertheless, it must interact with matter, otherwise it could not be detected or reflected or polarised, and interferometers could not produce fringe patterns. It must be scattered, reflected or re-radiated and thereby affect the state of the matter with which it interacts, to produce these various effects.

Although, as noted in the Introduction, dowsing is widely used in the building industry and on farms to locate underground pipes, cables and drains, water divining is a special branch of the technique practised successfully by only a small minority. The remarkable property that water has been found to display when it interacts with the fields produced by rotating masses may go some way towards explaining the special place that it has in the history of dowsing.

Most of our body weight is water, and we may now begin to understand dowsing, the ability to detect fields produced by rotating masses.

A room enclosed by aluminium will shield the body from the fields of the sun and the earth, a change that may be a health hazard.

CHAPTER 5

Further experiments and possibilities

From the outset, a primary objective of the research into dowsing pursued by the author and his colleagues had been to discover some means of making a detector system that does not involve the human body. It seemed ironical at the time these related researches into fields produced by rotating masses began, that not only had we failed in our primary objective but we found that hand-held dowsing detector rods provide the most sensitive, quick and reliable system available to detect the fields. They enabled us rapidly to begin making discoveries using our established techniques in dowsing interferometry and the new techniques in polarimetry.

The discovery of the special property of water offers the possibility that it may be used, as the body appears to use it, to make an inanimate detector system that will be sensitive and fast, for use in connection with both natural and laboratory generated fields.

Water, however, is not the only natural feature that interacts with the field; light is involved as well.

While measuring the interferometer pattern produced by the first interferometer in a pasture near Loch Rannoch one bright sunny evening, the sun set behind a local hill; it was still light but the pasture was no longer sunlit, yet the dowsing response disappeared instantly. I continued to walk back and forth along the usual track and after several minutes the pattern reappeared.

I thought no more about it until some years later when C. M. Humphries told me he had found that dowsing did not work without light and reminded me that another of our colleagues N. Duffy had reported some years ago that light had an effect on dowsing. These reminded me of the sunny evening by Loch Rannoch and led me to carry out experiments in the shielded laboratory to find out what effect light may have on the field produced by rotating masses. The results were as follows.

Light is not needed for a rotating mass to generate a field. The generator can be put in a light proof cardboard box and still gives a dowsing response.

Light is needed, however, on the ground where the dowser detects the field, and the strength of the detector response is proportional to the brightness of the illumination.

The worldwide interferometry carried out at all times of the day and night proved that the solar field passes through the earth but we do not know to what extent it may be degraded. For communication purposes it would be sensible to begin experiments with Morse code.

Furthermore, we do not yet know to what extent the field decreases with distance. Dowsing rods could be used to give some estimate of it but that has yet to be done over a considerable distance using a generator.

Shortly before a series of strokes affected my balance and deprived me of the ability to dowse, my wife and I had carried out some simple experiments using a bench grinder to generate a field and aluminium foil on a sheet of hardboard to intercept it, whereby my wife was able to transmit Morse code to me through a wall.

At that time ill health and family responsibilities prevented me from pursuing the experiments any further, but since the laboratory facilities needed to do so are small it seemed sensible for me to publish what I had already done in the hope that others might succeed in developing a compact inanimate detector.

Besides communication, other obvious applications of suitable detectors are as medical scanners and in astronomy.

We still do not know how the human body turns its interaction with the field into a rotation of hand-held dowsing rods, and research into that matter – a subject for medical physics I should think – may in itself provide information that will enable the development of a compact detector.

The field is reflected by aluminium paint on steel and by a silver coating on glass – good news for radio astronomers and optical astronomers, for whom the ability to detect rotating masses by this field would open up a vast range of opportunities from planetary astronomy to cosmology.

Since the laboratory experiments indicate that the strength of the field is proportional to the mass and to its angular speed of rotation, it may be reasonable to refer to it as the M–Omega Field.

References

(1) V. C. Reddish, 1993. *The D–Force*. Published by the author, Edinburgh.

(2) V. C. Reddish, 1998. Trans. Roy. Soc. Edinburgh: Earth Sciences, **89**, 1–9.

(3) Georgius Agricola, *De Re Meticalla*, Basel, 1556. This was translated in 1912 by the future President of the United States of America, Herbert Hoover. The most recent edition is H. C. and L. C. Hoover, Dover, N. Y., 1950.

(4) R. J. Dodd *et al.*, 2002. Trans. Roy. Soc. Edinburgh: Earth Sciences, **93**, 95–99.